Alain Marillac

INSTANT
RELAXATION

alain marillac

INSTANT
RELAXATION

Published by :
Editions de Mortagne
250, Industrial Boulevard
Boucherville (Quebec)
J4B 2X4
Tel. : (514) 641-2387

Translation :
Blanche Hodder

Cover Illustration :
Clic Communications

Legal deposit :
National Library of Canada
National Library of Quebec
October 1989

ISBN : 2-89074-906-1

1 2 3 4 - 89 - 92 91 90 89

Printed in Canada

*For those who made
the development of this technique possible
and those who need it.*

«The vital forces are those which press you forward. We do not have to name them. We just have to acknowledge them within ourself and within the others. In fact, we could not possibly identify them: they are a mystery. We can draw from the vital forces, we can rely on them, but we do not know exactly why.

Finally, I think that all of us have to ask his own questions and find his own answers. I cannot answer for someone else's questions.»

Martin Gray
Psyché, no 5, Nov. 78

CONTENTS

INTRODUCTION

The technique of instant relaxation is based on precise criteria and meets equally precise demands. A method was needed which could be learned quickly. (Schultz's self-directed training takes three months to be adequately mastered.) The technique also had to have maximum flexibility and be usable anywhere, in any position and without special equipment. Refining this technique took five years. In some ways, it is related to already existing techniques such as the Coue method II, will therapy, self-directed training, Jacobson's differential relaxation and biofeedback. Instant relaxation, in its final form, is a technique that can be learned in two to four hours alone, or in a day with a group. It permits relaxation in from several seconds to two minutes, depending on the individual, and can be done on a bus, in the subway, on a plane, in a nightclub or at a cocktail party. It also gives control over cold, heat and pain. With training, it leads to mastery of self-hypnosis and willpower reinforcement. In the latter case, instant relaxation is reinforced by bio-energetic techniques which are discussed in the second part of this book. Linking them can help you stop smoking or drinking, for example.

Many relaxation methods aim at an introspective analysis of the subject. The technique explained in this book aims first at letting you relax immediately in any situation, totally or one body part at a time. Naturally, this can open up many other possibilities which we will talk about farther on. This technique is particularly suitable for people who have to make a constant effort — actors, public speakers, salesmen, indeed anyone who must or who wishes to keep a clear mind and be full of energy at any moment of the day.

*

*　*

First, I will tell you how instant relaxation came to be. Five years ago, I was doing my military service and was put in a commando section. We had to go on long, high-speed marches; we had to run and jump almost constantly and had only a few minutes of rest. During my leaves, I re-read all the books on relaxation I could find but all the techniques took too long. What I needed was a quick way to recover because we often stopped only for 10 minutes or so.

So I put together different elements of various methods and tested them on myself one by one — and instant relaxation was created. After a month of trials, I succeeded at an effective synthesis which gave me a complete rest in three minutes. Also, when I was walking, I could relax my arms and my shoulders and only the muscles which were supposed to work did, while the others rested. I then taught the technique to my companions, which caused me to change a few details. It turned out that what worked for me didn't necessarily work for others. This helped me to refine and develop my technique and gauge its effectiveness through sustained observation.

Afterwards, I applied myself to giving maximum use to instant relaxation to make it the most beneficial self-control technique possible. I now propose to test these results on you and hope that you will get as much benefit from it as have those to whom I have already taught it.

*
*   *

PART ONE

I

PRACTISING INSTANT RELAXATION

Relaxation has an increasingly large place in today's world and operates as a reaction to the many stresses and strains of modern life.

In cities, human beings are mentally and physically subjected to aggression, especially noise, which increases constantly. People can only emerge triumphant from this non-stop confrontation if they possess suitable weapons and have a real awareness of the threats to them.

Pollution is undoubtedly the most common stress today. Indeed, it destroys or alters the environment and the person just as it does stone. For example, the statues in the Acropolis in Athens are being eroded by the sulfur dioxide present in the polluted atmosphere of the city. Noise causes increasing stress and accelerated organic deterioration. Disco dancing, for example, keeps the heartbeat elevated over periods of hours. The noise impairs hearing and we find an alarming increase in deafness among younger and younger people.

Cases of deafness have almost tripled in thirty years and many mental illnesses are also attributed to noise. When the effects of alcohol and tobacco are added to this, the human being has to fight minute by minute to remain healthy. In "Hygiene de la vie quotidienne," Jean Boyer notes that in a secretarial pool, decreasing noise by 20 decibels improved performance by 9% and reduced typing errors by 29%.

Noise wreaks havoc on the nervous system. Constant disturbances induce mental shock and, when daily problems are added, the slide into nervous depression can be extremely rapid at the least additional stress if the person has no way to react or fight.

Further on, we'll see that relaxation is an excellent method of retaining self-control and making a fast recovery, in any place and in any circumstances. However, we must not forget that other methods are within our reach, especially in North America. Nature walks around lakes or in forests are easy to do and provide calm, silence, solitude and cleaner air. Add even minimal physical activity to this to increase the body's muscular resistance and it will be easier to react to the many assaults of the environment upon returning to the city.

Apart from the stresses already mentioned, we see a sharp increase in cases of obesity and tension in modern life, which brings about an increase in cardiovascular illnesses. Mental illnesses are also constantly mounting. The number of tranquilizers and sleeping pills sold is unbelievable. This chemical therapy fosters an extraordinary contrast : thousands of people take sedatives to sleep and stimulants to help them through the day. The human being becomes something of a machine simply reacting to information input. However, there are many techniques being rediscovered which enable the person to react and find or re-find a normal life cycle. Self-control and relaxation are among them.

When practised and understood, these two techniques increase willpower and give greater control over muscles and internal organs. In the second part of this book, we will see how to use these techniques best, not only to combat fatigue, stress or insomnia but for self-conditioning to help you stop smoking or drinking and solve personal problems.

*
*　*

II

INSTANT RELAXATION TECHNIQUE

People are different : some fight and some surrender. As Lanza del Vasto says, there are people who are self-supporting while others perpetually lean on empty air and end up falling on each other. A person always supported by others is fragile, vulnerable and always dependent. Conversely, the men or women who know their inner possibilities, who know that at each moment of life they can draw on their own strength and energy to solve a problem or confront the turmoil of life, will know they are their own support and will not need the help of those around them to get back on their feet when they have to. As long as you cannot tap your inner strength, you are a perpetual supplicant; you will constantly angle for attention, help and support. If you know how to release your own potential, you will become active, a giver, not a taker. Actions and deeds follow on each other: you will be the giver, the coach, the leader in life. Tell yourself you must be either the locomotive or the wagon.

To be this kind of person, aware of your potential and abilities, you must know yourself, control yourself, know how to draw on yourself, cultivate your will and your energy and know your possibilities. From now to the end of the book, I will ask you to work alone, without detours and without cheating, so that having someone else around will not make you self-indulgent or lead you to fake your work, the study of your abilities.

My goal is to give you the means to cultivate your own strength, to awaken your energy and use it to succeed at what is important to you, whether it be self-assertion, getting a job or being able to appear in public without fear. If you agree to follow me on this path, I feel that you have already taken a step forward because you have decided to do something on your own initiative. I will ask you to take this step again at any moment, the first being the most difficult: now we can begin.

Before doing anything else, take a piece of paper and honestly write what you think of yourself and draw up a balance sheet of your life up to now : your trips, your meetings, your experiences, your abilities, professional, artistic, etc. In a word, put yourself on this piece of paper. Don't be self-indulgent about the faults you know you have and don't forget your good points.

You will now concentrate on your breathing ; it is one of the cornerstones of this technique. First, you must be convinced that you can influence it and you must understand its importance. Put your hand over your heart while breathing normally : your heart is beating regularly, calmly. Now breathe rapidly, as if you had just run long and hard. Now, control your heart ; it is beating quickly and jerkily. This shows you the direct action of breathing on the heart. Not only your heart benefits from good respiration ; the heart ensures that your whole body is oxygenated.

Instant relaxation uses three types of breathing derived from hatha yoga. The first and third methods will be used at home or in your car, when you are feeling calm. The second method will be the driving force of the technique. I have isolated this second method from the other two because many people feel ridiculous doing certain exercises on the subway or in public.

The goal of instant relaxation is to be usable by everyone, so the second type of breathing will serve as the relaxation "trigger" because it can be practised anywhere without anyone noticing. Now, let's look at the three kinds of breathing in order. (A short table at the end of the book will let you refer to the breathing plan throughout your reading.)

— The first type of breathing is to eliminate carbon dioxide from your lungs. Take a small breath with your mouth half-open, then exhale completely, puffing out your cheeks as if you had run for a long time. Repeat this exercise five (5) times.

— The second breathing type, the motor for what you're doing, is very simple. It is to calm and relax you while reinforcing body energy. Take a long breath through your nose, mouth closed, and exhale slowly and lightly — VERY LIGHTLY — through a half-opened mouth. This type of breathing will be used to trigger relaxation through a simple process which we will see farther on.

— The third type of breathing can be done at home, in your car or even standing in the street if you feel the need. It is meant to calm and cleanse the system ; it also helps self-control. Breathe in slowly through your nose, keeping your mouth closed : this inhalation should last around two (2) seconds. While doing this, contract your diaphragm and raise your ribs, without moving your head or neck which should remain very straight. Hold your breath while counting up to eight, then exhale through the mouth in one breath as if you were blowing out a candle. While exhaling, relax your diaphragm and slump your shoulders as much as possible. Repeat this five (5) times in a row; you can practise it alone when you need to recover rapidly.

*
*   *

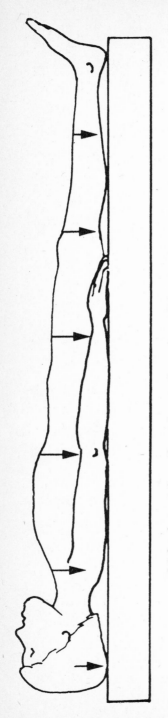

Make the weight and tension go down toward the mattress.

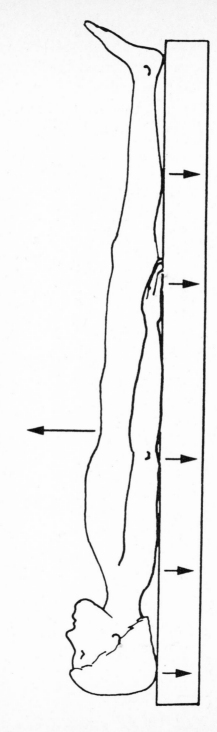

When the weight has gone, you will feel the lightness of your body.

I am now going to try to explain the instant relaxation technique simply and progressively. Often, I have to give long explanations of the process although it is extremely simple. You will be surprised at how easily you get results.

As you have already seen, you can, through your breathing, affect your heartbeat. Now, you are going to see how you can affect your right arm, for example. First get comfortable in an armchair or on a bed and close your eyes :

— Concentrate on your right arm ;

— Imagine that each of your muscles is an over-inflated balloon ;

— Imagine that each inhalation further inflates your muscles, inflate the balloons even more ;

— Now, exhale deeply, gently through your barely-open mouth and meanwhile feel all the muscles of your right arm deflate and relax. All your muscle balloons release the air filling them.

— Inhale and exhale again to confirm that your muscles are truly relaxed, that there is not the least contraction in your arm.

— Now, mentally compare your right and left arms. Become aware of the differences, feel the tension in the left arm in comparison to the relaxation of the right arm.

Now do the same thing for your left arm, deflate the balloons that have taken the place of your muscles. Breathe deeply through your nose for a long time while inflating all the muscles of your left arm, then breathe out completely while relaxing your muscles and totally deflating the balloons. Make sure no tension remains. Open your eyes and move your arms. One thing is very important to do from the beginning because this procedure will let you relax anywhere, anytime : synchronize breathing no. 2 and relaxation. For you, this kind of breathing must induce relaxation each time. They must be linked in your mind and in your training. BREATHING No. 2 = RELAXATION.

*
* *

For now, you have succeeded at separately relaxing your right and left arms. This is called differential relaxation. It will allow you afterwards to relax any part of the body you want while the rest remains tense.

We will now go on to complete training in this "piecework" relaxation. It is always done in the same order to help you develop the habit and then the reflex which, with practice, will trigger instant relaxation of any muscle or, at your choice as we will soon see, induce numbness in any part of the body. The order is as follows and is in five steps : right arm, left arm, two legs at once, shoulders and torso, head.

30

Why both legs together, you may ask. This is one of the small modifications I made while developing my technique. At first, I recommended relaxing the left leg, then the right. With practice, I realized that many people cannot mentally dissociate their lower limbs. Most people unconsciously see them as a whole. So, as instant relaxation is the goal sought, I now advise relaxing both legs at once and, I must say, the results have been excellent.

You are now going to test this relaxation cycle on yourself and do it repeatedly to accustom yourself to the BREATHING-RELAXATION combination. Afterwards, a single breath will trigger total bodily relaxation.

Go back to your earlier comfortable position and bring about the relaxation of your right arm : a long inhalation which inflates the muscles, prolonged exhalation which loosens them totally and leaves them relaxed. Do the same thing for the left arm. Be sure no tension remains. To make it easier, imagine that the air from your muscle balloons is escaping through your fingertips. Now that both these limbs are relaxed, concentrate on both legs at once. Breathe deeply through the nose, as you have already learned to do, and inflate the muscles of your thighs, calves, feet and hips. Exhale completely while imagining the air from your muscle balloons going all down your legs to leave your body through the tips of your toes, leaving your legs limp and relaxed. Be sure no muscles are contracted. If necessary, breathe again.

Now, breathe in again, and your entire inner body will inflate. Exhale and all your internal muscles, all your insides loosen, relax and rest at once. Be sure there is no tension left.

Now, concentrate on your head and your face. Inhale while being very conscious of all your facial muscles. Exhale while relaxing the muscles of your forehead, let your cheeks go, relax the muscles around the eyes, let your lower jaw fall without opening your mouth.

Inhale again and exhale, feeling all your body relaxed, perfectly limp, at rest. You will feel good, very good.

Perfect. Now you've experienced your first differential relaxation, your first selective instant relaxation. Before going farther, you will make several informal try-outs. Move, walk or run in place to bring back the tension in your muscles or, if you prefer, wait until tomorrow. But you must succeed at inducing this selective instant relaxation on command and for any limb. Try the left arm ; you are comfortable, inhale and the muscles inflate, exhale and the relaxation is instantaneous, the air from your muscle balloons escapes through your fingertips. Perfect. Now, the same way, try the head alone, then the torso alone, etc. Repeat this exercise as often as possible ; in a very short time, you should find it easy to relax any of the five areas : right arm, left arm, legs, torso, head.

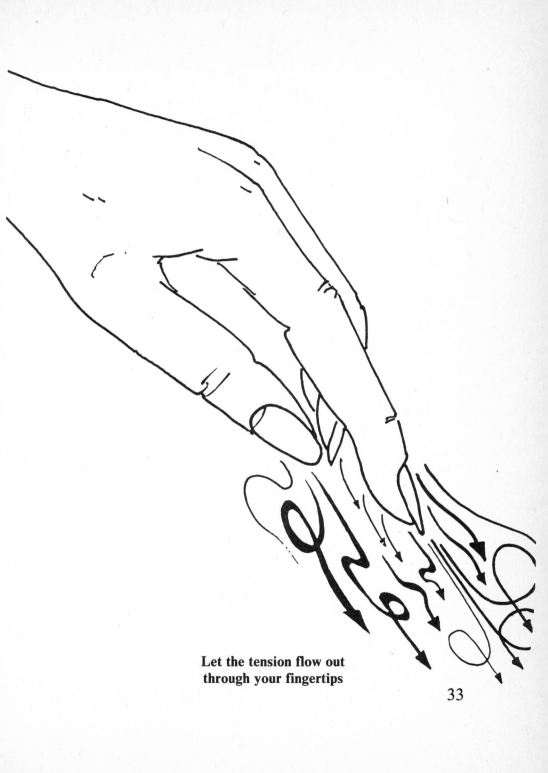

**Let the tension flow out
through your fingertips**

33

Now, you should be able to slip into the relaxation mode without much trouble. Try to relax your legs separately ; this can be very useful, as we'll soon see, in case of an accident, for example.

But the important thing from now on is that you succeed in the step that follows. At the moment you know how to rest, how to relax yourself limb by limb instantaneously. Now you must be able to obtain full INSTANT RELAXATION.

This full relaxation will be useful every day ; it will allow you to recover very quickly and rest even if you only have three or four minutes to spare. This mental and physical relaxation is absolutely necessary in today's life. It allows you to remain clearminded at any time of the day. What businessman would not be happy to know that he can be as efficient at the end of the day as in the morning ? This is possible, no matter what your occupation. The deliveryman who doesn't stop running around all week can, in the subway, for example, relax totally and stay mentally and physically fit for the evening. In "Training an Actor", Stanislavsky tells about a very talented actress who could only rarely reach the peak of her abilities ; at a tragic moment in her performance, her right eyelid would contract, sometimes very slightly. He advised her to try to relax all her facial muscles when she came to the difficult passages. When she succeeded, all the muscles of her body relaxed spontaneously. She was transformed. Her body became light, her

34

features mobile and expressive, her sensitivity came out.

I myself remember a case somewhat similar when I was making an information tour on hypnosis, suggestion and relaxation. A young singer came to see me. She was devastated because she had to perform that evening before a large audience. It was the first time she had performed in a concert hall and she had lost her voice. Her stagefright was so intense that her throat and her body were tense and contracted. After deep relaxation and some suggestions for strengthening her will, she went on and was very successful.

These examples show you the importance of bodily relaxation, a technique which lets you relax your muscles at once; it will be useful all your life.

Again, get comfortable in your armchair or on your bed and take a long breath through your nose, inflating your lungs, pushing out your ribcage, filling your muscle balloons, ALL the muscles of your body this time. Exhale through slightly parted lips and all at once relax all the muscles of your body, from your head down to your toes, pushing the air from your muscle balloons down through your body and letting it out through the tips of your toes. Be sure there is no more tension in your body. Inhale and exhale again if necessary. Repeat this exercise several times, then bring back the centres of tension in your body. You have to completely master the selective relaxation technique, part by part, and the full Instant Relaxation before going on to the rest of this book. Only by mastering the instant relaxation technique can you go on to the next steps.

*
*   *

III

USING THE THREE
BREATHING TYPES
AND INSTANT RELAXATION
WHILE STANDING

Wanting to relax while standing may seem a little surprising at first, but many people work standing up or have to remain that way for long periods, if not all day. Thus it is very useful to know how to relax in this position.

The first step is to find your own centre of gravity, the position that requires the least muscular effort.

To do this, stand up straight. Now, let yourself sway forward and backward; you will feel your leg muscles react to keep you balanced. Between the two positions where your muscles are working, there is a moment when there is almost no muscular tension in your legs; this is the position you must adopt.

As soon as you have found it, do breathing number 2, which induces bodily relaxation. You will notice that your upper body, arms included, relax and that your legs eliminate all the muscular tension not needed for balance.

Do this exercise several times and when you have completely mastered it, complete it, if you can, with breathing number 3, which will let you "recuperate" faster and will strengthen your self-control.

This exercise is particularly useful for salespersons, bartenders and anyone who has to remain standing for long periods as well as for people who like to dance the night away and stay fresh and energetic. It's also very good for people who, for business or pleasure, go out for social evenings or cocktail parties. In the latter cases, you frequently have a glass in your hand and if you practice instant relaxation while standing you may have a few accidents; that's where selective instant relaxation comes in.

For example, you're standing, your glass in your right hand. Using breathing number 2, relax your left arm, your head, your torso and your legs, keeping only the tension needed for balance. However, maintain the tension in your right arm so you don't drop your glass. Once relaxed, all you have to do is bring your left arm back to normal tension and transfer your glass to it so you can then relax your right arm.

Of course, if you feel you need to recuperate more fully, you can add breathing number 3.

*
*   *

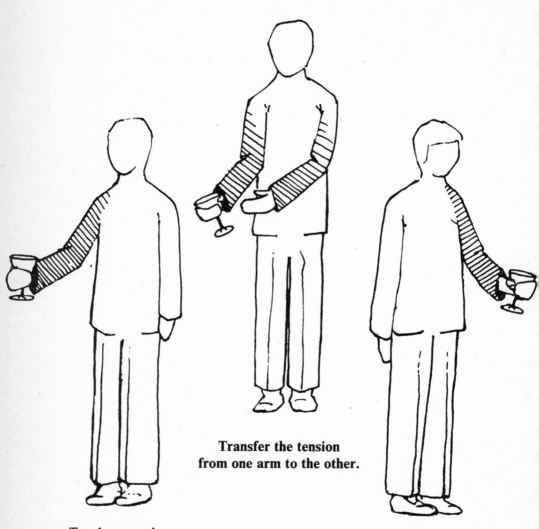

**Transfer the tension
from one arm to the other.**

**Tension remains
in the right arm.**

Relax the right arm.

You are now going to go on to a new step, trying out full instant relaxation with the three types of breathing.

The first time you do it, you will be seated or lying down, then standing. To begin, practise the first type of breathing: a small inhalation through half-open mouth, then exhale completely, puffing out your cheeks as if you had just run a long time. Now, do the second type of breathing, with which you are already familiar and which induces total body relaxation. Don't worry if you feel a little "drunk" the first time; it's normal. Linking these two types of breathing often has this effect, which disappears with practice.

As soon as you are relaxed, breathe calmly, tranquilly and regularly. Then go on to the third type of breathing, which completes the relaxation and restores your energy. Later, we will see how to magnify this energy. Inhale slowly through your nose, keeping your mouth closed. Hold your breath while counting calmly to eight (8), then let out all the air at once as if you were blowing out a candle.

Repeat all the exercises we have just covered, because with this short chapter, your basic training in instant relaxation ends. You will now be able to test its effectiveness on yourself, with experiments that will be very useful to you and, who knows, may some day even help you survive in difficult situations.

*
*   *

IV

DIFFERENT
PHYSICAL CONTROLS

The first tests will deal with climate, as this is the
element we confront most often, particularly cold
weather in Quebec.

How can you use instant relaxation to combat
cold or heat? Well, we're not going to combat it;
we're going to adapt to it, become one with it. Most
people huddle in on themselves when they feel cold.
They tense their muscles to make a kind of obstacle.
In bad weather, we must play the part of water,
which molds itself to its container; we must be the
wall of sand, which lets water infiltrate and pass

through and remains standing, while a brick wall resists and ends up breaking.

Yes, instant relaxation can teach you to "be" the cold or the heat, instead of enduring them. This is what you are going to try now. We will begin simply with the temperature of the room you're in. Sit or remain standing, as you wish. Now, try to feel the temperature of the room on your skin, try to harmonize with the very air of the room. I know this is not easy at first; imagine a multitude of little antennas on your skin which pick up the air around you, its temperature.

As soon as you are in touch with the temperature, you will discover a difference between your body and the room which you were not aware of a moment ago. If this difference now feels quite clear to you, make yourself shiver, make a long shiver go down your spine. You will notice that this shiver re-establishes the equilibrium between your body and the room.

You have just completed your first adaptation to a temperature. It wasn't very difficult because the difference was small but now we'll try something else. Get busy for a moment, attend to your affairs, so that your unconscious brings back the gap that existed previously; also, raise the room temperature by several degrees. You now have the right conditions for going on to the second experiment.

44

For the second time, go into a state of total instant relaxation. As before, you will "feel" the room temperature on your skin; it's warmer than during the first experiment. Become totally aware of this difference. Shiver several times or once but as long and as strongly as possible. Become one with this temperature, let it melt into you. Try to merge with it, identify with it, become it.

To get more into practice, accentuate the differences, always remaining preoccupied with the heat alone. If while you're reading this, it's cold outdoors or snowing, go out for a moment and come back in. As soon as you're inside, relax completely and blend into the temperature around you.

Repeating this exercise will let you adapt to temperature in any place, a little like animals who hibernate and lower their body temperature.

*
*   *

Let's do the same thing with cold. It may seem more difficult because we are always somewhat afraid of cold. If it's winter outside, this exercise will be simpler to do; if not, do it during the evening when there's a small, cooling breeze. The simplest way is to go out on your doorstep wearing a sweater. Breathe calmly at first, then do breathing number 2, which makes you relax. After that, induce a long shiver down your spine, several times if necessary, which will merge you with the air around you and the cold. Don't put up any obstacle to the cold; let it flow through you. Don't do this exercise if you have a cold, because your body will not have its natural adaptive ability — unless of course you are stuck on a highway in the cold and snow. Then you will have to use all your weapons against intemperate weather. In such a situation, practise breathing number 3 regularly; it will help you get through the ordeal by augmenting your energy.

*

*   *

V

PAIN

After heat and cold, let's tackle something that frightens us much more: PAIN.

Fear of pain is very common, even for trivial things such as an injection at the doctor's office. Paradoxically, this kind of mild pain frightens us most. If you slice your hand with a knife, the pain will be less intense because it is unexpected. The reverse happens at the doctor. We know the needle is coming and we have time to think about it. The real cause of the pain is our imagination. We often find the same behavior in the face of death. J.C. Barker in "Shintoism" cites several cases where people who believed they would die, did die from the fear of death they felt.

The influence of the mind on the body has been demonstrated by Freud and psychoanalysis. Psychosomatic medicine starts from the principle that all illness has a meaning and practically every affliction hides psychological problems. To simplify, psychosomatic medicine reasons like this : the mind expresses itself through the body and the body through the mind. In Japan, the Seichono-ie religion goes farther and says illness is a direct product of the mind and does not exist in itself. The body becomes what the mind thinks, what the imagination invents. For many sick people, the pathological condition follows from a failure of will.

Physical conditions with a mental cause are seen every day : an angina attack may come from a broken engagement, an ulcer from a period of unemployment, deafness from having noisy people around, etc.

So, we consider that the mental has a direct effect on the physical, and thus on pain. We are going to see how, with the help of the instant relaxation you have mastered, you can control and conquer pain.

There are several ways to achieve this discipline. For example, some people prefer to live with the pain until it reaches its peak and then cancels itself out by its very intensity. This method, it must be admitted, requires great willpower and self-control. So I prefer to describe a simpler technique here which acts as a mental anesthetic.

Sit in an armchair. Using breathing number 2, relax just your left arm. Concentrate strongly on it. Now, bring up images of snow, of cold which will invade your left arm alone. Close your eyes to facilitate the feeling. "SEE" the ice cover your arm, "FEEL" the cold seize it. It is as if this limb were slowly becoming inert, dead, frozen.

Mentally order yourself to retain this feeling even with your eyes open and for at least a minute. Repeat this order several times, while feeling the cold in your arm alone, from fingertips to shoulder. Open your eyes and note that the feeling still exists, that your left arm is still inert, cold, icy. With your right hand, pinch your left arm. You should feel almost nothing. Wait a minute and feel the difference when your mental order has lost its effect. Pinch yourself again to feel the difference.

Repeat this exercise several times to fully master it. Later you will see that this simple training can be useful more often than you would think.

Now put a needle or a pin close to you. Don't think of the prick, imagine nothing. Concentrate again on your arm and bring back the intense cold. You know now that cold lessens and even eliminates feelings and pain. Think only of making your arm as icy as possible, see the frost cover it until you feel nothing more than a block of ice, alien to your body. Now, make suggestions to yourself as you did earlier, give yourself commands :

— My arm will stay like this for a minute, even if I open my eyes. It will remain icy cold and I will feel nothing, even if I bang it against a wall. My arm will stay like this, feeling nothing for a minute, even if I open my eyes.

Repeat these words until you are completely sure that they have penetrated deep into your brain. Now, open your eyes and see that your arm is still inert. Pinch it : you should be able to pinch very hard now, without feeling anything, your mind still fixed solely on the feeling of cold. Without deviating from this image of numbness and cold, take your pin and prick your left arm. You will be surprised at how little you feel, no pain at all. Go easy, though, because I have seen people push a needle completely into their arms, they were so concentrated and surprised at the same time. It is not necessary to push it in deeply. Prick your arm in several places to really see how numb it is.

Do this exercise several times and change arms. As soon as you have the ability to control pain, try it on your legs and your cheeks. If you want to astonish your friends, you will be able to pierce your cheek without feeling anything, like a professional fakir. But that's a bit beside the point for our purposes.

Practise regularly and with this training you will be able to control unpleasant feelings — at the dentist, for example, when he hasn't given you a local anesthetic. It will also be helpful if you are in an accident. Suppose you have a broken leg or a deep slash on your arm ; you will be able to concentrate on the injured limb and make the pain disappear or, at least, reduce it considerably. This procedure also constricts blood vessels and reduces blood loss, which can prevent haemorrhaging.

You will need regular training to fully master this and you will have to practise assiduously once you have done so. I think it's worth it, considering the possibilities it offers.

If you have several injuries, go into total instant relaxation with suggestions — cold and numbness commands to the whole body. Let's now look at how you can use instant relaxation for a small but frequent problem : a headache.

Here I'm talking about an ordinary headache that comes on suddenly and inconveniences you for a day, not about chronic headaches which need medical or psychoanalytic attention.

O.K., you have a headache and you don't know what to do. First, move your head, turning it from side to side two or three times. Bend it forward, bring it down to the left shoulder, then back and around to the right shoulder, then again forward. Do this several times ; this movement eliminates tension in the base of the skull and the neck. Using breathing number 2, relax your shoulders and head, totally relax your face. Breathe calmly, deeply, regularly, then concentrate on your head, imagining it inside a large balloon. See your headache like black smoke inside your skull. Now work at making this smoke come out of your head and go into the surrounding balloon. Get the smoke out until there is none left inside your skull. Be sure all the smoke has come out into the balloon. When that is done and there is no trace of the smoke inside your skull, imagine the balloon soaring aloft with all smoke rising inside it, buoying it up. The balloon flies off, clears your head and climbs into the sky or goes out the window and goes far away from you. When it is quite far away, make it burst and you will see the black smoke of your headache disappear.

To conclude, practise breathing number 3 and go back to what you were doing before ; your headache has disappeared.

*
*   *

VI

NOISE

In brief, you now possess selective instant relaxation, total instant relaxation, the ability to relax standing up, as well as the ability to use instant relaxation to control heat, cold and pain, and a method to get rid of a headache. At this stage, you are better able to judge the technique's usefulness, but we still have other uses to look at — such as, for example, how to relax in noisy surroundings. Now we can broach this subject, because you know how to relax completely in less than a minute, or at least in a very short time, if you have followed the preceding exercises carefully.

Whether you are in a discotheque, the subway or a bus, all sorts of noises assault you. How can you relax in these circumstances?

To do this exercise, get next to a radio, a stereo or any other source of loud sound. Get as comfortable as possible. Close your eyes and listen to all the sounds around you: voices, music, automobiles, household appliances, etc. Try to mix all the sounds into a single humming; concentrate on all the sounds at once, not any one sound in particular. You will notice that they all blend into a kind of mixed vibrating buzz.

Then, try to modulate this single sound in your own way by listening more or less attentively, mentally moving it away and bringing it closer. This will probably take a number of tries but in the end it's relatively simple. Apply yourself to doing this first step correctly; repeat it several times.

Relaxation in the middle of noise.

Now that you've managed to do this easily, you can still go a little farther. Relax, put yourself into total instant relaxation, and again merge all the sounds around you into a single sound, then mentally make the single sound go away and come back regularly in a to-and-fro movement. As soon as you get the rhythm, imagine the sea, its waves advancing and receding constantly. The single back-and-forth sound will slowly become the sound of the sea, the rhythm of the waves.

Add an image of the sun above you and concentrate totally on the idea of the sea and the sun, which will relax you even more. Enjoy your sense of well-being.

In this exercise, as in the cold exercise, you have to adapt to the environment, use it to make yourself feel better, rather than expend energy fighting it. You are borrowing a technique from judoka where, instead of opposing your adversary, you use his strength against him. Know how to take the things that disturb you and make them serve you.

With training, you will instantly get the sound of the sea and the feeling of warmth from the sun which can also help you combat cold.

Of course, you can imagine something other than the sea. As soon as you can control the noises around you, you can make the single sound you create into anything you want, simply by giving it your own rhythm.

*
*   *

PART TWO

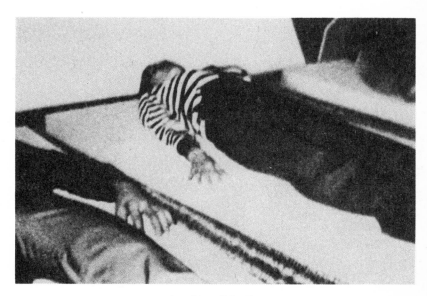

A relaxed body

DEEP INSTANT RELAXATION AND ITS USE THROUGH WILLPOWER REINFORCEMENT

In this second part, we will leave the physical realm to dwell more particularly on using instant relaxation as a way to solve mental problems. For this, we will use a deep form of total relaxation ; we'll begin with this.

You'll be better off lying down for deep instant relaxation. Begin with breathing number one to eliminate carbon dioxide from your lungs. Then, practise breathing number two and go into total instant relaxation. Now, breathe regularly, slowly, calmly and very deeply. Try to think of nothing, let yourself go down as far as possible, almost to the edge of sleep by giving yourself mental commands, suggesting that you be calm, relaxed. You can say, for example :

— I feel good, very good, and I am going deeper and deeper into the relaxed state. I feel better and better, my breathing is calm and regular, and I feel good...

As soon as you are completely relaxed, begin breathing number three which will awaken your brain without tensing your body. You are now in the state needed for analyzing a problem or fighting a bad habit. However, before explaining how to proceed, you must understand a certain number of mechanisms.

*

* *

The word personality comes from "persona" which was a mask worn by an actor in a play, defining his role. The personality is thus conditioned by the role you play each day and by the face you make for yourself. People around you react to your mask, to what you show them. If, for instance, you are always sad, it's unlikely that the people who approach you will be overflowing with joy ; you will only attract those who resemble you. The unconscious further amplifies this state through gestures. Jung points out that we are not clearly aware of the position of our bodies in space, of certain gestures or facial expressions. So, many people create enormous problems for themselves simply because they do not project their vitality but a forbidding, sad and blocked image.

This is the time to try to get out of it, to react and find movement, gaiety and health. Anything can be used, because we must not forget that all the mental and physical representations around us inform the unconscious and imprint the information received, which will be constantly usable just as any sensation is. A person who had learned instant relaxation told me one day that she was in the habit of going to relax outdoors in Lafontaine Park in Montreal. She experienced an insight into her behavior at the beginning of the winter while concentrating on one of the pools that had been emptied. In a deeply relaxed state, the image of the pool came back to her and she understood then that the container is not much of anything without a content. This pool was sad and useless without the water which gave it life. Because of this simple observation, this person changed her life radically, began to dress in brighter colors and returned to university where she discovered a soulmate.

Another example of these curious "clicks" in the unconscious : a young boy who lived only through his favorite celebrities, was failing in school and couldn't succeed at anything. During a session, just before he went into deep instant relaxation, I got the idea of showing him a photo album containing pictures of his favorite singers and actors. In the middle of these photos, I put a mirror to show him that the only LIVING thing that responded to him was himself. He thought it over in the relaxed state and since then, he may not be the head of his class but he has really come to terms with himself.

The role of relaxation in self-analysis is certainly not negligible. L. Auger writes that, in response to emotions and problems, there are the same methods of understanding and solution: sports and various activities for the body, repose and relaxation for the sensory motor processes, and modification of thinking through inner sentences related to real happenings. Lowen keeps to this idea by saying that a person who reviews his or her possibilities and potential will become aware that personal goals can be reached without leaning on others. He or she will become aware of the fact that any failure is energy potential for a coming success, a stimulus for a second attempt.

Some people would say it is not necessary to relax to deal with one's problems or to take a good look at oneself. This may be so, but we must not forget that any kind of problem can cause nervous and even physical fatigue in the human being. And fatigue of any kind diminishes vital potential; it has repercussions on all the faculties and weakens them. A reduction in spontaneous attention, concentration, memory and association of ideas follows. It is a kind of disorganization of the organism's responses, a dimming of most faculties. Relaxation will restore these functions and allow existing problems to be analyzed effectively.

Let's go on to practise. Choose one of the problems you now have. Write it on a sheet of paper. Now, go into the deep relaxation described at the beginning of this chapter: Lie down, first breathing, second breathing and total instant relaxation; breathe tranquilly, regularly. Go into the relaxation as deeply as possible. Now, practise the third breathing, which awakens the brain. Proceed according to the diagram below, imagining five boxes in your head:

Event or problem to analyze or understand;	Impressions, thoughts, feelings about it;	Changes caused in my life by this problem;	Inconveniences it causes;	Advantages to get from it.

In the first box, write your problem. Let's take a simple example as an illustration: "I want to play a sport but I don't have time."

With the problem stated as simply as possible, go on to the second box and write all your ideas in any order: I want to be a champion but I'm not capable; it's tiring; I would be in shape, etc.

Our example doesn't lend itself well to the third box, which is more appropriate for work-related problems, but let's try anyway. Changes caused in my life by this problem ? : I walk less than I used to ; I use my car more ; I get tired too easily ; I don't play enough with my children ; I eat more ; my clothes no longer fit me, etc.

Now the fourth box, the inconveniences : I am overweight ; my children are not as close to me ; I spend too much on gas, etc.

The fifth box can be adapted to the problem. If the problem is irreversible, write all the advantages, no matter how slim, which arise from the situation. For example : "I'm unemployed." In the fifth box, you write : I have more time for my family ; I'll use this time to take classes in retraining or upgrading, which will increase my chances of going back to work, etc.

The second way of using this box is : The solution : I practise no sport and yet that makes me spend more money, gives me less time with my family, etc., so I'll get up 15 minutes earlier in the morning and do exercises ; I'll walk a little instead of always taking the car ; I'll make myself play with my children to help me lose weight, etc.

This box system, which can be arranged to suit your case, will always provide you with solutions if, of course, you are completely honest with yourself and are not being self-indulgent.

*
* *

Here is another shorter method for solving your problems. This method uses only two boxes and will undoubtedly be of use to some of you.

This has happened and there is no way to go back on it.	How to make this happening useful, see its advantages, transformations and inconveniences and modify all that into a positive pattern.

Then get down to giving yourself orders and suggestions dealing with the positive side of your conclusions. Bring up the details and actions which will make you become what you want to be. Make yourself act. My personal method of getting myself to do things which are displeasing or frightening is to tell my friends I am going to do it. By saying it, the time comes when I have no choice but to act.

*
* *

To go even farther in this method of instant relaxation, you must know how to come out of the relaxed state while retaining all your energies. To do this, when your analysis is over or if you simply want to come out of deep relaxation feeling thoroughly fit, concentrate on the centre of your chest and imagine a small point of light. Feel this point in the centre of your chest, feel the heat emanating from it, watch it become a small yellow sun, brilliant and hot, which is growing slowly and filling your chest. Feel the gentle heat of this sun, feel the rays stealing through your arms, your legs, your head. Now, the sun itself has occupied all your body, warming your muscles, giving them strength and vigour.

Become aware that this sun is your energy, your inner strength manifesting itself, making itself known. This strength, this energy is there, it is present and even when you open your eyes, you will still feel it. You can come out of the relaxed state; you feel your own strength throughout your body, your living energy, and you will be able to awaken it at any time now, simply by going to the end of your deep instant relaxation.

To illustrate this final phase of instant relaxation and also to review the analysis technique, I now suggest you follow me through a relaxation to stop smoking. I have to point out that this will not work unless you really want to stop smoking; you must be strongly motivated. To be effective, this session should be repeated twice a week for two weeks and once a week for another two.

Sit in a chair or on your bed. Try to feel the seat or the mattress under your body as much as possible. You must be aware of each point of contact. Do the first breathing, then the second, and put yourself into total relaxation. Be sure that no muscular tension remains, that your whole body is completely relaxed.

Set up a screen inside your head and draw four boxes on it. In the first box, put all the reasons that make you smoke, review each of your excuses and pretexts. Go over them in detail; take your time.

In the second box, imagine a cigarette and take it apart : unglue the paper and shred the tobacco so you realize that this cigarette is only a tobacco leaf placed on a sheet of paper, that it is really only two sheets rolled into one.

Compare the first and second boxes. Do these two sheets really meet your needs, the reasons you have described? Reflect seriously on this.

In the third box, write all the possible replacements : work, sports, solving inner conflicts, etc. Be sure these meet your expectations. When you have done this, go on to the next box.

In this last box, there is a little sun that you will bring to the centre of your chest and let it radiate throughout as we did a little earlier. This is your willpower, your energy shining in you, and its strength will make your whole body vibrate.

Now, become aware that the cigarette no longer has the same importance for you. You know that even if you see a cigarette, even if you buy them for someone else, even if you touch one or someone offers you one, you will have no more desire, no more wish to light one. Thoroughly feel this willpower in you that erases your desire to smoke because all your being knows and has analyzed how unimportant the cigarette is to you.

Repeat the suggestion process before opening your eyes. Tell yourself again how unimportant the cigarette is to you and how it can be easily replaced by the solutions you wrote in the third box. You will be able to rediscover this energy, this will not to smoke, whenever you want by putting yourself in the relaxed state.

Of course, this technique will have to be repeated several times, always with the inner will to stop smoking... or to stop drinking or overeating. Let's look again at the illustration for reinforcing willpower.

Causes ;	Problem ;	Replacement solutions ;	Energy, willpower.

*

* *

SOME ADVICE

This chapter will supply you with some advice to help you stay in shape as long as possible and, this way, prolong the effects of instant relaxation. Some of it is mere detail but when repeated can help you accomplish a task more completely or succeed at expressing yourself totally.

First, posture : keep yourself straight and loose, in a vertical position which is the resting position. There are people who radiate great dignity because they hold themselves upright. Peace emanates from them ; people feel safe around them.

Breathe with the chin in, the head, neck and trunk kept in alignment. With your mouth closed, inhale through your nose ; this helps respiration and circulation of energy which passes through the spine and clears the mind. Keeping your mouth closed gives better breath control. A tucked-in chin keeps the muscles of the neck firm and the spinal column straight.

When you get up in the morning, one of the best ways to fill yourself with energy is to do several physical exercises to increase body temperature and speed up circulation to the muscles. Then, take a cool shower and, if you feel like it, finish with a good rubdown. Be self-confident, try never to doubt yourself; your guiding principle should be that EVERYTHING IS POSSIBLE for you.

To prove this, make yourself do something special each day, something you are not in the habit of doing. For example, ask directions from someone in the street even if you know your way perfectly well. This helps you make contact with strangers. Telephone for information on any product, etc. All these actions will give you increased self-confidence and help you gradually eliminate all the tensions that come from thoughts such as : "Will I be good today ?", "Is my work really good ?", "Will I have the courage to tackle it ?", etc. Be more and more sure of yourself. If you have the time and the opportunity, practise a sport; it will give you an ease of action as well as suppleness and elegance in your movements.

Eat enough but always leave room for more ; it will keep your resistance up and eliminate the drowsiness that follows too heavy a meal.

Write your goals on a sheet of paper and note all the steps to be taken. Then, take them ONE BY ONE.

*

*   *

To sum up, you have to draw up a BALANCE SHEET of yourself now, determine your mode of ACTION and strengthen your AUTONOMY. Become aware of your POSSIBILITIES and use them in your HABITS to create HARMONY in your life, reinforced by proper ORGANIZATION of your time and activities. Fortify your MIND so you will always have an unbeatable MORALE. By using all the possibilities of instant relaxation, increase your ENERGY and your EFFICIENCY. You will certainly notice many TRANSFORMATIONS in yourself and your life.

I will list all the important words. Remember them ; they can change your life.

B : Balance sheet
A : Action and autonomy
P : Possibilities
H : Habits and harmony
O : Organization
M : Mind and morale
E : Energy and efficiency
T : Transformation

These are the points and all the important phases of your personality, its awakening and its blossoming.

*
*   *

INTRODUCTION
TO SELF-HYPNOSIS

Self-hypnosis, as its name indicates, is placing oneself in a state of hypnosis and awakening at one's convenience. Self-hypnosis is thus linked to the history of hypnosis. The powering force of self-hypnosis, like instant relaxation, is suggestion. The orders you give to your subconscious, to yourself, act and cause a result.

You must only start this section after you have completely mastered deep instant relaxation; from there, it will take little time to induce it. If you have practised properly, you should be capable of reaching this state in less than ten minutes.

The following step consists of inducing this state in any position. You will feel this relaxation whether seated on a chair or on a stool or in a soft armchair; avoid the standing position, however. Take the time you need for this exercise because training and repeated practice are the keys to success in rapid self-hypnosis.

Self-hypnosis is the special use of precise suggestions in a state of relaxation. With instant relaxation, you are already used to doing both. Now you have to go a little farther. How?

As with deep instant relaxation, you start practising lying down, so you'll feel more at ease. Practise the first breathing : inhale with the mouth half-open, then exhale, puffing out your cheeks as if you had just run a long time. Then, go on to breathing number two : trigger total body relaxation, while breathing regularly and calmly. Let yourself go as deep as possible into a relaxation that increases with each moment. Use suggestion to increase the effect of the relaxation which, for the moment, is only a state of deep instant relaxation. In the present case, however, you do not go on to the third breathing ; instead, you continue to use suggestion. Modify the suggestions as you go along in whatever way you like. We will take an example :

A student who wants to learn a text by heart will read it several times at the beginning, paying attention to each word, each comma, each period. Then he will reread the text very quickly without paying attention to the content and aloud, if possible. Then he will get on his bed and practise the first breathing, followed by the second, which triggers deep instant relaxation. Then he uses suggestion : first he deepens the relaxation. Afterwards, slowly, he will add without making an effort, without any special concentration, sentences like : "In an hour, I will know the text by heart ; it will be written down to the last detail in my mind and I will remember it perfectly. In an hour I will know the text by heart ; my reading will be printed indelibly on my brain and I will retain every detail. In an hour I will know the text by heart."

At this stage, you are now in a state of self-hypnosis. Now you must simply repeat to yourself that "in an hour I will come out of this state." Repeat this suggestion several times as a precaution. Then let yourself be taken over by the well-being into which you are slowly slipping. At that point, something strange and very pleasant often happens : it is as if you were sleeping peacefully while in reality you know you are not in a natural sleep. You know you can wake yourself at any time. Above all, don't try to analyze this state : in any case, you shouldn't feel any desire to because you feel so wonderfully good. You will wake up normally at the time you have decided. For the first few times, it's better to make the experience last at least half an hour to enjoy the pleasant sensations thoroughly.

This state I have just talked about is very difficult to describe but it is easily and, I'd say, almost naturally triggered. Why can you only reach it after the suggestion process? Simply because this state logically follows on deep relaxation. While your mind is letting your suggestions through, the self-hypnosis state cannot be completely reached because there is no real "disconnection" from your intellect. As soon as you let yourself go, it appears.

Of course, you can make additional suggestions to reach this particular state of self-hypnosis, but this hardly seems necessary to me. However, if you have difficulties, you can repeat suggestions such as: "Between now and counting to three, my mind will become completely detached and I will plunge into a state of deep hypnosis which I will come out of in ✕ minutes (choose the duration). This state will be very pleasant and I will not be aware of anything. My relaxation is increasing now (1) and is becoming more and more profound; all my body, including my head, is becoming heavier. I don't want to think anymore (2), I am going deeper and deeper down into sleep; a deep, refreshing sleep...During this sleep, my mind will learn my text, retain it and when I wake up in ✕ minutes, I will know it by heart (3). I am falling asleep!"

Personally, I feel it is better to attain this state — which appears by itself, I repeat, after deep instant relaxation — without practising the third breathing. The sequence automatically brings on the

80

state of self-hypnosis. On the other hand, suggestions designed to bring on the state can, at the beginning, wake up a vigilant and attentive consciousness because you are expecting a sleep effect without knowing which one. Unconsciously, you may feel a fear of the unknown. Thus, it is probable and normal that you may not reach the self-hypnosis state for the first few times.

It also sometimes happens that this hypnotic state changes into normal sleep. Don't worry about it ; with practice, you will manage to keep complete control of these variations. Now all you have to do is hypnotize yourself as quickly as possible. This is why at the beginning of the chapter, I emphasized triggering instant deep relaxation in any place and in the shortest time period possible. If you have applied yourself to that, you should reach it within eight to ten minutes. Then, link your suggestions to what you want to obtain and let the self-hypnotic state come by itself. Half an hour later, wake up feeling great.

Repeating this exercise will teach you to recognize the difference between "deep relaxation" and "self-hypnosis". Self-hypnosis really gives the impression of no longer being anything, of having neither body or mind.

When you have become perfectly skilled at differentiating these two feelings, create a short sentence that pleases you or find an image that you like. This sentence or image will trigger self-hypnosis in the same way the second type of breathing triggers instant relaxation. Let's suppose, for example, that you take the image of the cover of this book. When you want to induce self-hypnosis, you only have to think of the cover. With practice, it will become your signal for hypnotic sleep. So, in order, to induce self-hypnosis, you must:

— do the first breathing,
— then the second, triggering instant deep relaxation,
— accentuate the relaxation through suggestion,
— do not induce mental alertness,
— make suggestions to yourself about a precise desire,
— let the relaxation become self-hypnosis by itself or help it come with suggestions,
— put a precisely timed wake-up command in the suggestions and suggestions for well-being,
— wake up feeling great.

With a little training and using a key symbol such as an image, you will soon manage to hypnotize yourself at super speed. However, at the beginning, to fully master the technique, take the time to feel all the changes in sensations you may have. These sensations usually vary with the person, even though there are certain general impressions.

Don't use a too-common image as a key-signal for triggering hypnosis. Some very sensitive or suggestible people can fall asleep anywhere or involuntarily. An example : if you have taken an advertisement of a product as a signal and you are very emotional, you may hypnotize yourself every time you see this photo. So choose a fairly uncommon image or object that will be yours alone.

*
*   *

CONTRAINDICATIONS

I'm often asked : "Is self-hypnosis dangerous ? Would it be unadvisable to practise it in some cases ?"

The same rules hold for self-hypnosis and hypnosis — or nearly so, since the risks of having an incompetent hypnotist are eliminated when you are your own practitioner.

Apart from that, it is advised that people who have or have had psychotic problems or special problems such as epilepsy or serious heart disease avoid practising self-hypnosis. In this case, deep relaxation MUST suffice.

There is another contraindication that I call "a situational worry" and some people are victims of it. These people, once in the hypnotic state, do not completely control their muscles and if they are seated, for example, will half-collapse in their seats. Most people, however, keep their starting position. If you are in the first category (which you will find out by trying in the presence of witnesses), avoid practising self-hypnosis in public places or you may end up with a crowd around you trying to revive you — because this slump really looks like a fainting spell.

This is why I call it a situational worry. Because of the sudden attention you may get, you also risk a rude awakening. If, in spite of everything, you must practise in a public place, tell someone or be sure to be well propped-up on your seat or, again, if possible, lie down.

If you still have some fears, practise self-hypnosis only at home. For the rest, be happy with deep relaxation, reinforced by suggestion, and then after several moments, go on to the third breathing. The suggestions will still work although not as strongly.

The current trend of using Walkmans can help you practise self-hypnosis in public places : you can use sound as a key-signal, a kind of music that aids relaxation.

Altogether, self-hypnosis generates many advantages and multiple possibilities.

While self-hypnosis can strengthen your will, it also plays a part in knowing yourself better. We have already seen how to analyze a problem with instant relaxation; you can further this research using self-hypnosis.

Many behavioral and sexual problems or temporary disabilities originate from frustration which is often not recognized at the conscious level. If you use instant relaxation to look at the different possible causes of a problem, you can use self-hypnosis to solve the problem once and for all.

This self-analysis which is within your grasp can often become your best therapeutic tool : let's take one or two examples to help you understand this :

In general, a phobia is a conditioned reflex resulting from a frightening experience often occurring in childhood. One of the most common cases is a fear of elevators. If an adult with this fear goes into in a state of instant relaxation and, using only his everyday memory, looks for the moment his fear began, he will undoubtedly find, first, a few scraps of information, leading him to discover at least the precise date of the event which caused the phobia. After several tries, interspersed with self-hypnosis sessions designed to awaken memories, he will discover, for example, that once some friends shut him into an elevator and he didn't know how to get out. The fact of finding himself alone, shut into a frightening place for a child, caused a rejection of this device and a subconscious denial characterized by distress each time he got into an elevator as an adult.

Looking for the time when this person was shut in is already the first step to a cure. When the cause of the fear is discovered, it must be relived. In this case, the best thing is to see the scene again with adult eyes and visualize oneself as so little that the elevator buttons are too high to reach. Then, try to look at the comic aspects of the situation while still watching it coolly. Most of the time, this will be enough to eliminate the fear forever.

Each time we manage to laugh at our distress, it loses the frightening and threatening aspects which transform it into fear.

Self-hypnosis can then be used to strengthen willpower when faced with the elevator and return it to its mundane appearance since it is no longer a source of fear.

For any fear or problem, the important thing is to find the cause in order to bring about the cure. If an electrical wire has been cut, you can certainly change the plug, but the current still won't come through. You have to find the break to make the wire function normally again. There are two ways to do this : when you are acting alone for yourself, deep relaxation with mental awakening and a deliberate search for the cause of your problem ; or triggering self-hypnosis using the suggestion of an instantaneous appearance of the cause of your problem when you wake up. This, it has to be said, is most useful for minor problems. If the cause is serious, this procedure may trigger other problems, so it is better to work with a specialist.

The causes of most of the little temporary troubles of daily life are fairly easy to find. For example, I remember a friend who had attacks of sudden weakness. It would happen all at once; he would suddenly feel an overwhelming fatigue and couldn't keep his eyes open. All he wanted to do was lie down and sleep. He couldn't understand why it happened so suddenly and always in the evening, without warning.

After several tries with self-hypnosis, he realized that this wave of tiredness always happened the evening before an important meeting. These meetings intimidated him; he felt he wasn't up to them. His unconscious then acted to give him an excuse and he felt feeble and unable to do anything. On three occasions, he had to cancel or postpone the meetings or have someone replace him. He knew it was damaging his career, but he was unable to do anything about it. After finding the cause of his problem during his self-hypnosis sessions, he began to use suggestion to reverse the phenomenon. In fifteen days, he managed to increase his energy before the difficulties, so much so that an important meeting gave him additional strength and amplified his will-power. He had overcome his handicap.

Instant relaxation, backed up by self-hypnosis, can serve each of us. It doesn't require a lot of effort and is a rapid and effective method, you will soon see. In daily life, work or play, there are a thousand uses for this technique. Even in hospitals, it can be used to stimulate patients and help them recover more quickly. This is easily observed when people who are in a hurry to get better are compared with those who really don't care. For the same illness, the former come out of hospital sometimes a week or two earlier than the latter. This is how you harmonize your actions and your mental force. As Socrates said : In a good and useful life, action and thought unceasingly uphold each other.

*

*   *

Bibliography

Alexander F.   La médecine psychosomatique
                                Éd. Payot – Paris 1952
Auger Lucien   S'aider soi-même
                                Éd. de l'homme – Ottawa 1974
Beaudoin Charles   Suggestion et autosuggestion
                                Éd. Delachaux et Niestlé Paris –
                                1938
Bechterev   La suggestion et son rôle dans la
                                vie sociale.
                                St. Petersbourg – 1909
Boon Henri, Davou Yves   La Sophrologie
et Macquet Jean Claude   Éd. C.E.P.L. – Paris 1976
Charpentier Raymonde   L'autosuggestion
                                Éd. des Champs-Élysées
                                Montargis 1958
Chauchard Paul   La médecine psychosomatique
                                Éd. P.U.F. coll. Que sais-je
                                No 656 – Paris 1974

Eisenbud J. — The psychology of headache
Psy. QII 592 1937

Freud Anna — Le moi et les mécanismes de défense.
Éd. PUF – Paris 1969

Filioux J. — L'inconscient
PUF – coll. Que sais-je
Paris 1967

Geisman P. et de Bousingen D. — Les méthodes de relaxation
Éd. Dessart – Paris 1968

Gray Martin — Les forces de la vie
Éd. Robert Laffont – Paris 1975

Hebb D.O. — Psycho physiologie du comportement
Éd. PUF – Paris 1958

Horney Karen — L'auto analyse
Éd. Stock – Paris 1953

Janov Arthur — Le cri primal
Éd. Flammarion – Paris 1975

Jarreau R. — Technique de la méthode Jacobson
ouvrage collectif – Éd. Expression scientifique – Paris 1959

Jeanson G. — L'accouchement sans douleur
Éd. du Seuil – Paris 1954

Laing R.D. — Soi et les autres
Éd. Gallimard – Paris 1971

Lowen Alexander — La dépression nerveuse et le corps
Éd. du Jour-Tchou – Paris 1975

Lowen Alexander — La bio-énergie
Éd. du Jour-Tchou – Paris 1976

Lupasco Stéphane — L'énergie et la matière psychique

Luthe Wolfgang — Autogenic Therapy
Éd. Grune et Stractton – New York 1973

Nuttin Joseph

Psychanalyse et conception spiri-
tualiste de l'homme
Éd. Beatrice Nauwelaerts – Paris
1968

Palmade Guy

La psychothérapie
coll. Que sais-je – Éd. PUF N° 480
Paris 1973

Rager G.R.

Hypnose, sophrologie et médecine
Éd. Fayard – Paris 1973

Rogers Carl et
Kinget Marian

Psychothérapie et relations
humaines
Éd. Nauwelaerts – Paris 1972

Rouet Marcel

Relaxation psychosomatique
Éd. Amphora – Paris 1972

Soubiran G.B.

Psychomotricité et relaxation
psychosomatique

Stanislavski Constantin

La formation de l'acteur
Éd. Payot – Paris 1963